Jim and the Big Fish

Maverick
Early Readers

'Jim and the Big Fish'
An original concept by Clare Helen Welsh
© Clare Helen Welsh

Illustrated by Patricia Reagan

Published by MAVERICK ARTS PUBLISHING LTD

Studio 3A, City Business Centre, 6 Brighton Road,

Horsham, West Sussex, RH13 5BB

© Maverick Arts Publishing Limited August 2018

+44 (0)1403 256941

A CIP catalogue record for this book is available at the British Library.

ISBN 978-1-84886-363-7

www.maverickbooks.co.uk

This book is rated as: Yellow Band (Guided Reading)
This story is decodable at Letters and Sounds Phase 3/4.

Jim and the Big Fish

by **Clare Helen Welsh**

illustrated by **Patricia Reagan**

Jim is at the dock.

He has his net.

It is a big net.

"I will get a big fish!"

he says.

Jim dips in the net but...

...down swoops a bird.

"Shhhhh!" says Jim.

He misses the fish and pulls up
a sock!

Jim dips in the net but...

...down swoops a bird.

"Shhhhh!" says Jim.

He misses the fish and pulls up a boot!

"Shhhhh!" says Jim.

"I cannot fish!"

He pulls up a hat!

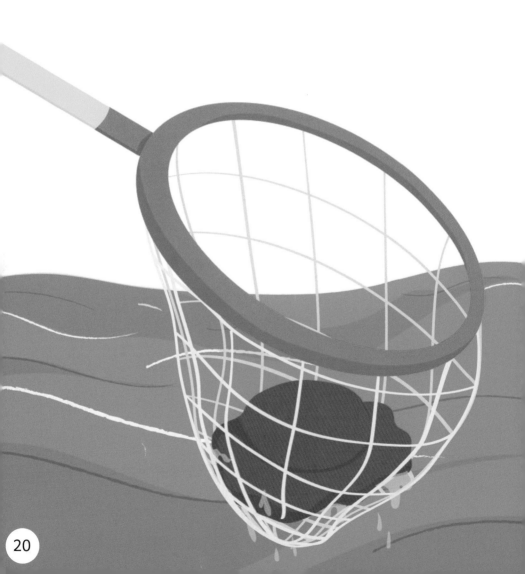

Jim has a sock and a boot
and a hat...

…but no fish.

The man gets his sock and
his boot and his hat back.

And Jim gets...

... a big fish!

Quiz

1. Where is Jim?
a) At a shop
b) At a dock
c) At a park

2. What does Jim use?
a) A bucket
b) A fishing rod
c) A big net

3. What animals were naughty?
a) The birds
b) The cats
c) The dogs

4. What colour is the fish?
a) Yellow
b) Pink
c) Green

5. What does Jim get for giving the things back?
a) A big hug
b) A big net
c) A big fish

Turn over for answers

Book Bands for Guided Reading

The Institute of Education book banding system is a scale of colours that reflects the various levels of reading difficulty. The bands are assigned by taking into account the content, the language style, the layout and phonics.

Maverick Early Readers are a bright, attractive range of books covering the pink to purple bands. All of these books have been book banded for guided reading to the industry standard and edited by a leading educational consultant.

To view the whole Maverick Readers scheme, visit our website at

www.maverickearlyreaders.com

Or scan the QR code above to view our scheme instantly!

Quiz Answers: 1b, 2c, 3a, 4b, 5c

HOPSCOTCH
TWISTY TALES

Puss in
Football Boots

by Sam Watkins and O'Kif

W
FRANKLIN WATTS
LONDON•SYDNEY

This story is based on the traditional fairy tale,
Puss in Boots, but with a new twist.
You can read the original story in
Must Know Stories. Can you make
up your own twist for the story?

Franklin Watts
First published in Great Britain in 2016 by The Watts Publishing Group

Text © Sam Watkins 2016
Illustrations © O'Kif 2016

The rights of Sam Watkins to be identified as the author
and O'Kif as the illustrator of this Work have been asserted
in accordance with the Copyright, Designs and Patents Act, 1988.

ISBN 978 1 4451 4794 9 (hbk)
ISBN 978 1 4451 4796 3 (pbk)
ISBN 978 1 4451 4795 6 (library ebook)

Series Editor: Melanie Palmer
Series Advisor: Catherine Glavina
Series Designer: Peter Scoulding
Cover Designer: Cathryn Gilbert

Printed in China

Franklin Watts
An imprint of
Hachette Children's Group
Part of The Watts Publishing Group
Carmelite House
50 Victoria Embankment
London EC4Y 0DZ

An Hachette UK Company
www.hachette.co.uk

www.franklinwatts.co.uk

MIX
Paper from
responsible sources
FSC® C104740
FSC
www.fsc.org